Books Boost Business

Illustrated by Nimeshika Dulanjani Gunarathna.

Copyright 2020 by Amanda Hill Ryall

All rights reserved

No part of these pages, either text or image may be used for any purpose.
Therefore, reproduction, modification, storage in a retrieval system or retransmission, in any form or by any means, electronic, mechanical or otherwise, for any reasons is strictly prohibited withour prior written permission.

ISBN First published 2020: Books Boost Business

Book:  The Mood Munchers – Let Me Out  Amanda Hill Ryall

ISBN-13: 978-1-913501-14-3

# THE

# MOOD

# MUNCHERS

Hi! We are the Mood Muncher family, we live in the rainbows and are always ready to help children with their emotions and feelings

Blaze loves the warmth as it keeps his flame alive. He needs to find the right place to settle down and is always on the lookout for children who are getting cross. He loves to jump inside and help them.

When he is annoyed, he looks like a bright-red colourful flame.

When he becomes frustrated, he grows and his colours get darker.

When he is cross, his flame shoots up and becomes bigger. It gets even higher when he gets angry!

Blaze guzzles his energy when he gets furious and can even turn into a rage!

Let me out!
I need to be seen!

His energy and flame seeks
children who are getting cross as
he wants to come out to play.
"Let me out," he shouts, "I need
to be seen."

Suddenly, Blaze can see where he is needed. Two children are fighting over an ipad, pulling it and shouting at one another.

In jumps Blaze; the little boy is annoyed with his sister as she is trying to take his ipad. As she shouts at him he is getting madder and madder. So Blaze heats up his flame and becomes angrier! The boy's face turns red and he is shouting back at his sister.

Arrggh! Blaze can feel his energy increasing, flames building until........
The boy is furious and pushes his sister to the ground and snatches back his ipad.

Uh Oh! Looks like a member of Blaze's family has turned up in the little girl. She is crying and Blaze can recognise the colour of the sad mood – it's his brother Blue.
Blaze does not like it when Blue spoils his fun as he has to grow smaller.

As his flames reduces, the boy runs out of the room, slams the door and sprints outside into the cool air, where he sits down in a shady spot.

As the cold air rushes in Blaze realises that the boy is taking deep breaths - lots of them - 10 in all!

The angry feeling is getting smaller and smaller until the boy is just annoyed. Blaze is back to his original size.

Wow! He thought, that fire didn't last long.

This boy knew how to calm himself down, by going outside to a quiet spot and to take 10 long, slow deep breaths.

The boy has calmed down and suggested that he and his sister shares the ipad. She is happy once more to be playing with her brother.

Oh no! Looks like another member of Blaze's family is joining in...Ray full of beams of happiness. The children have made up and are happy......time for Blaze to go!

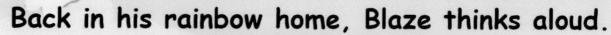

Back in his rainbow home, Blaze thinks aloud.

Blaze knows he is a powerful feeling and better out than in.

Good bye for now. See you again soon. There are more of us to meet!

This book is the first in a series that I have been inspired to create to help children engage and understand their emotions. I have loved this opportunity to support children and their parents and teachers.

Thank you Laura Helen Herbert for igniting my love of creating books to share my message – you are an amazing light!

Thank you to my awesome illustrators Nimshii for your diligence and willingness to listen and respond to my visions – you are amazing!

Thank you to my husband Martyn and son Alessandro for your enthusiasm in allowing me the space to create.

Thank you to my tribe and Anna Garcia for continued loving support and for being my greatest cheerleaders.

Thank you to all the children I have ever taught for teaching me patience and showing me what you need.

Thank you to you for choosing this book. I hope you love it.

Amanda Hill Ryall is passionate about children and their wellbeing. Working in early years and primary schools both in the UK and abroad she has supported the learning and personal development of hundreds of children. Amanda is also an inspiring mother and aunt and understands that children can be different at home from how they react at school.

Having had the opportunities to work both in the state and private sectors for nearly 30 years, Amanda realised that all young children are similar; they are born with a thirst of curiosity and adventure to grow and become.

Cultures, backgrounds and views in society can affect children's vision. Amanda wants all children to realise that they are complete and can choose how they interact and respond to different situations each day. Believing and trusting yourself is key to loving and growing and allows life to present all types of opportunities and miracles says Amanda.

As human beings Amanda knows that the human part of us has emotions that can affect our lives. Our being part is deep within us all.

Through her books Amanda wants children to realise that they are human beings, part of a wide world and will encounter many adventures and meet many people.

Being able to be aware of your feelings as an interested observer will allow children to let their emotions arise, be and leave without any judgement or fixation on them.

As an ELSA (Emotional Literacy Support Assistant) Amanda has helped children sit with their emotions and let them pass.

Through stories she allows younger children to view and understand feelings in a safe, fun way. Hence she created the series The Mood Munchers where children will meet emotions such as fear in the character Jitters, anger through the fiery character Blaze, sadness through Blue and Ray who is full of happiness.

Children are the future and can teach us so much. Enthusiastic to supply tools to help, Amanda created The Mood Munchers to allow parents, teachers and children to be with their emotions in a loving, amusing way.

# Ray Shines
# Turn That Frown Upside Down

By Bestselling Author Amanda Hill Ruall

# JITTER JUMPS

By Best Selling Author Amanda Hill Ryall

# WHOA! THAT WOE!

By Best Selling Author Amanda Hill Ryall

# Help Blaze Return Home